INNER REFLECTIONS

Engagement Calendar 2019

SELECTIONS FROM THE WRITINGS OF
PARAMAHANSA YOGANANDA

SELF-REALIZATION FELLOWSHIP

FRONT COVER:
The Wanaka Tree, Lake Wanaka, New Zealand
Photograph by Tom Mackie
Design by Russell Frye

NOTE: *Holidays and other observed dates are included for the United States (U.S.), Canada, United Kingdom (U.K.), Australia, and New Zealand (N.Z.).*
Moon phases, equinoxes, and solstices are based on Pacific Standard Time (UTC – 8 hours).

Self-Realization Fellowship, 3880 San Rafael Avenue,
Los Angeles, California 90065-3219, U.S.A.

Printed in Italy
4845-J5440

The scenery of mountains painted on the ever-changing azure canvas of the sky, the mysterious mechanism of the human body, the rose, the green grass carpet, the magnanimity of souls, the loftiness of minds, the depth of love — all these things remind us of a God who is beautiful and noble.

—Paramahansa Yogananda

THE PHOTOGRAPHS IN THIS CALENDAR are accompanied by selections from the writings of Paramahansa Yogananda, whose timeless and universal teachings have awakened many — of all races, cultures, and creeds — to a deeper awareness of the one reality that sustains and unites us all.

Whether spread over the vast heavens or hidden in the exquisite delicacy of a tiny flower, nature's beauty is always beckoning, inviting us to look behind the outward form and sense the presence of God within.

We hope that the thoughts and images in these pages will bring you inspiration and encouragement in the days and weeks of the coming year.

The Wanaka Tree, Lake Wanaka, New Zealand   Photograph by Tom Mackie

With the opening of the New Year, all the closed portals of limitations will be thrown open and I shall move through them to vaster fields, where my worthwhile dreams of life will be fulfilled.

—Paramahansa Yogananda

Ice shelf, Weddell Sea, Antarctica Photograph by Frans Lanting

December/January

31
monday

1
tuesday
New Year's Day

2
wednesday

3
thursday

4
friday

5
saturday
Paramahansa Yogananda's Birthday New Moon ●

6
sunday

DECEMBER 2018

S	M	T	W	T	F	S
						1
2	3	4	5	6	7	8
9	10	11	12	13	14	15
16	17	18	19	20	21	22
23/30	24/31	25	26	27	28	29

JANUARY

S	M	T	W	T	F	S
		1	2	3	4	5
6	7	8	9	10	11	12
13	14	15	16	17	18	19
20	21	22	23	24	25	26
27	28	29	30	31		

7
monday

8
tuesday

9
wednesday

10
thursday

11
friday

12
saturday

13
sunday

First Quarter ◐

JANUARY

S	M	T	W	T	F	S
		1	2	3	4	5
6	7	8	9	10	11	12
13	14	15	16	17	18	19
20	21	22	23	24	25	26
27	28	29	30	31		

FEBRUARY

S	M	T	W	T	F	S
					1	2
3	4	5	6	7	8	9
10	11	12	13	14	15	16
17	18	19	20	21	22	23
24	25	26	27	28		

Although you find glimpses of the Divine, don't be satisfied;
go deeper within, and you will sit at the brink of eternity facing God.

—Paramahansa Yogananda

Cote d'Or at sunset, Seychelles   Photograph by N. Sorokin/AGE Fotostock

I open the gates of the human limitations of family, caste, color, and creed.
I am racing everywhere to feel again my consciousness of omnipresence.

—Paramahansa Yogananda

Wild horses, Torres del Paine National Park, Chile   Photograph by Londie G. Padelsky

January

14
monday

15
tuesday

16
wednesday

17
thursday

18
friday

19
saturday

Full Moon ◯

20
sunday

JANUARY

S	M	T	W	T	F	S
		1	2	3	4	5
6	7	8	9	10	11	12
13	14	15	16	17	18	19
20	21	22	23	24	25	26
27	28	29	30	31		

FEBRUARY

S	M	T	W	T	F	S
					1	2
3	4	5	6	7	8	9
10	11	12	13	14	15	16
17	18	19	20	21	22	23
24	25	26	27	28		

January

21
monday
Martin Luther King, Jr.'s Birthday (Observed)

22
tuesday

23
wednesday

24
thursday

25
friday

26
saturday
Australia Day (Australia)

27
sunday
Last Quarter ◑

JANUARY

S	M	T	W	T	F	S
		1	2	3	4	5
6	7	8	9	10	11	12
13	14	15	16	17	18	19
20	21	22	23	24	25	26
27	28	29	30	31		

FEBRUARY

S	M	T	W	T	F	S
					1	2
3	4	5	6	7	8	9
10	11	12	13	14	15	16
17	18	19	20	21	22	23
24	25	26	27	28		

The more you meditate, the more you will realize there is Something behind the kingdom of ordinary consciousness where a great peace and happiness reign.

—Paramahansa Yogananda

Wasatch Mountains, Utah   Photograph by Howie Garber/AnimalsAnimals

Only in the castle of God can we find protection.
There is no safer haven of joy than in His presence.
When you are with Him, nothing can touch you.

—Paramahansa Yogananda

Church Rock, Red Rock Park, New Mexico   Photograph by Tim Fitzharris/Minden Pictures

January/February

Australia Day (Observed)

28
monday

29
tuesday

30
wednesday

31
thursday

1
friday

JANUARY

S	M	T	W	T	F	S
		1	2	3	4	5
6	7	8	9	10	11	12
13	14	15	16	17	18	19
20	21	22	23	24	25	26
27	28	29	30	31		

FEBRUARY

S	M	T	W	T	F	S
					1	2
3	4	5	6	7	8	9
10	11	12	13	14	15	16
17	18	19	20	21	22	23
24	25	26	27	28		

2
saturday

3
sunday

February

4
monday

New Moon ●

5
tuesday

6
wednesday

7
thursday

8
friday

9
saturday

10
sunday

February

S	M	T	W	T	F	S
					1	2
3	4	5	6	7	8	9
10	11	12	13	14	15	16
17	18	19	20	21	22	23
24	25	26	27	28		

March

S	M	T	W	T	F	S
					1	2
3	4	5	6	7	8	9
10	11	12	13	14	15	16
17	18	19	20	21	22	23
24/31	25	26	27	28	29	30

Come, Spirit! Come with the glory of the dawn;
come with the vitality of the sun; come through the portals of our silence.

—Paramahansa Yogananda

Sunrise, Monument Valley Navajo Tribal Park, Arizona   Photograph by Tom Till

Have only love in your heart for others.
The more you see the good in them,
the more you will establish good in yourself.

—Paramahansa Yogananda

Lynx kittens, Montana   Photograph by Robert Barber/AKM Images

February

11
monday

12
tuesday
First Quarter ◐

13
wednesday

14
thursday
St. Valentine's Day

15
friday

16
saturday

17
sunday

February

S	M	T	W	T	F	S
					1	2
3	4	5	6	7	8	9
10	11	12	13	14	15	16
17	18	19	20	21	22	23
24	25	26	27	28		

March

S	M	T	W	T	F	S
					1	2
3	4	5	6	7	8	9
10	11	12	13	14	15	16
17	18	19	20	21	22	23
24/31	25	26	27	28	29	30

February

18
monday
Presidents' Day

19
tuesday
Full Moon ○

20
wednesday

21
thursday

22
friday

23
saturday

24
sunday

February

S	M	T	W	T	F	S
					1	2
3	4	5	6	7	8	9
10	11	12	13	14	15	16
17	18	19	20	21	22	23
24	25	26	27	28		

March

S	M	T	W	T	F	S
					1	2
3	4	5	6	7	8	9
10	11	12	13	14	15	16
17	18	19	20	21	22	23
24/31	25	26	27	28	29	30

We should bathe our spirits in the deep, pure feeling that stirs within us when we gaze on the glories of His creation. This is the way to know God as beauty.

—Paramahansa Yogananda

Spirit Island, Jasper National Park, Alberta, Canada   Photograph by Michael Wheatley

The mind is a perfect instrument of knowledge when you have learned to base your life on truth. Then you see everything in a clear, undistorted way, exactly as it is.

—Paramahansa Yogananda

Oak tree and snow geese, Sacramento Valley, California   Photograph by John Hendrickson

February/March

25
monday

Last Quarter ◑

26
tuesday

27
wednesday

28
thursday

1
friday

FEBRUARY

S	M	T	W	T	F	S
					1	2
3	4	5	6	7	8	9
10	11	12	13	14	15	16
17	18	19	20	21	22	23
24	25	26	27	28		

2
saturday

MARCH

S	M	T	W	T	F	S
					1	2
3	4	5	6	7	8	9
10	11	12	13	14	15	16
17	18	19	20	21	22	23
24/31	25	26	27	28	29	30

3
sunday

March

4
monday

5
tuesday

6
wednesday
New Moon ●

7
thursday
Paramahansa Yogananda's Mahasamadhi

8
friday

9
saturday
Sri Yukteswar's Mahasamadhi

10
sunday
Daylight Saving Time begins (U.S. and Canada)

MARCH

S	M	T	W	T	F	S
					1	2
3	4	5	6	7	8	9
10	11	12	13	14	15	16
17	18	19	20	21	22	23
24/31	25	26	27	28	29	30

APRIL

S	M	T	W	T	F	S
	1	2	3	4	5	6
7	8	9	10	11	12	13
14	15	16	17	18	19	20
21	22	23	24	25	26	27
28	29	30				

O Spirit, I worship Thee as beauty and intelligence in the temple of Nature.

—Paramahansa Yogananda

Maroon Creek, White River National Forest, Colorado Photograph by Londie G. Padelsky

I am Thy babe of eternity, safe in the cradle of Thine omnipresent bosom.

—Paramahansa Yogananda

Mother polar bear with cub, Wapusk National Park, Manitoba, Canada   Photograph by Thomas Cooper

March

11
monday

12
tuesday

13
wednesday

First Quarter ◐

14
thursday

15
friday

16
saturday

St. Patrick's Day

17
sunday

March

S	M	T	W	T	F	S
					1	2
3	4	5	6	7	8	9
10	11	12	13	14	15	16
17	18	19	20	21	22	23
24/31	25	26	27	28	29	30

April

S	M	T	W	T	F	S
	1	2	3	4	5	6
7	8	9	10	11	12	13
14	15	16	17	18	19	20
21	22	23	24	25	26	27
28	29	30				

March

18
monday

19
tuesday

20
wednesday

Vernal Equinox Full Moon ○

21
thursday

22
friday

23
saturday

24
sunday

MARCH

S	M	T	W	T	F	S
					1	2
3	4	5	6	7	8	9
10	11	12	13	14	15	16
17	18	19	20	21	22	23
24/31	25	26	27	28	29	30

APRIL

S	M	T	W	T	F	S
	1	2	3	4	5	6
7	8	9	10	11	12	13
14	15	16	17	18	19	20
21	22	23	24	25	26	27
28	29	30				

You are a part of the Eternal Life. Awaken and expand your consciousness in God so that your concept of yourself ceases to be limited to the little body.

—Paramahansa Yogananda

Val d'Orcia, Tuscany, Italy   Photograph by Tom Mackie

Give goodwill to all, but develop a state of consciousness wherein nobody can ruffle you.

—Paramahansa Yogananda

Eastern bluebird, Marion County, Illinois   Photograph by Richard & Susan Day

March

25
monday

26
tuesday

Last Quarter ◑
27
wednesday

28
thursday

29
friday

MARCH

S	M	T	W	T	F	S
					1	2
3	4	5	6	7	8	9
10	11	12	13	14	15	16
17	18	19	20	21	22	23
24/31	25	26	27	28	29	30

APRIL

S	M	T	W	T	F	S
	1	2	3	4	5	6
7	8	9	10	11	12	13
14	15	16	17	18	19	20
21	22	23	24	25	26	27
28	29	30				

30
saturday

Daylight Saving Time begins (European Union)
31
sunday

April

1
monday

2
tuesday

3
wednesday

4
thursday

5
friday

New Moon ●

6
saturday

7
sunday

April

S	M	T	W	T	F	S
	1	2	3	4	5	6
7	8	9	10	11	12	13
14	15	16	17	18	19	20
21	22	23	24	25	26	27
28	29	30				

May

S	M	T	W	T	F	S
			1	2	3	4
5	6	7	8	9	10	11
12	13	14	15	16	17	18
19	20	21	22	23	24	25
26	27	28	29	30	31	

God is present right on the throne of peace within you.
Find Him there first and you will find Him in all the noble pursuits of life,
in true friends, in the beauty of nature, in good books, in good thoughts,
in noble aspirations.

—Paramahansa Yogananda

Springtime on Martha's Vineyard, Massachusetts Photograph by Paul Rezendes

Sit quietly in meditation to hear the voice of Divine Peace singing softly.

—Paramahansa Yogananda

Great blue heron, British Columbia, Canada Photograph by Michael Wheatley/AGE Fotostock

April

8
monday

9
tuesday

10
wednesday

11
thursday

12
friday

First Quarter ◐

APRIL

S	M	T	W	T	F	S
	1	2	3	4	5	6
7	8	9	10	11	12	13
14	15	16	17	18	19	20
21	22	23	24	25	26	27
28	29	30				

MAY

S	M	T	W	T	F	S
			1	2	3	4
5	6	7	8	9	10	11
12	13	14	15	16	17	18
19	20	21	22	23	24	25
26	27	28	29	30	31	

13
saturday

14
sunday

15
monday

16
tuesday

17
wednesday

18
thursday

19
friday

Passover begins Good Friday Full Moon ○

20
saturday

21
sunday

Easter Sunday

APRIL

S	M	T	W	T	F	S
	1	2	3	4	5	6
7	8	9	10	11	12	13
14	15	16	17	18	19	20
21	22	23	24	25	26	27
28	29	30				

MAY

S	M	T	W	T	F	S
			1	2	3	4
5	6	7	8	9	10	11
12	13	14	15	16	17	18
19	20	21	22	23	24	25
26	27	28	29	30	31	

The more you develop flowerlike divine qualities,
the more God will reveal to you His secret omnipresence in your soul.

—Paramahansa Yogananda

Flowering dogwood tree, Ozark Mountains, Arkansas   Photograph by Londie G. Padelsky

Be as simple as you can be; you will be astonished to see how uncomplicated and happy your life can become.

—Paramahansa Yogananda

Pasture, Cades Cove, Tennessee Photograph by Mary Liz Austin

April

22 monday

Easter Monday (All except U.S. & Scotland) Earth Day

23 tuesday

24 wednesday

25 thursday

26 friday

Last Quarter ◑

APRIL

S	M	T	W	T	F	S
	1	2	3	4	5	6
7	8	9	10	11	12	13
14	15	16	17	18	19	20
21	22	23	24	25	26	27
28	29	30				

27 saturday

MAY

S	M	T	W	T	F	S
			1	2	3	4
5	6	7	8	9	10	11
12	13	14	15	16	17	18
19	20	21	22	23	24	25
26	27	28	29	30	31	

28 sunday

April/May

29
monday

30
tuesday

1
wednesday

2
thursday
National Day of Prayer

3
friday

4
saturday
New Moon ●

5
sunday

April

S	M	T	W	T	F	S
	1	2	3	4	5	6
7	8	9	10	11	12	13
14	15	16	17	18	19	20
21	22	23	24	25	26	27
28	29	30				

May

S	M	T	W	T	F	S
			1	2	3	4
5	6	7	8	9	10	11
12	13	14	15	16	17	18
19	20	21	22	23	24	25
26	27	28	29	30	31	

Practice the art of living in this world without losing your inner peace of mind. Follow the path of balance to reach the inner wondrous garden of Self-realization.

—Paramahansa Yogananda

Common spotted orchid, Somerset, England Photograph by Guy Edwardes

If you appeal to God as the Divine Mother, She quickly gives in, for you have appealed to Her tenderness and unconditional love.

—Paramahansa Yogananda

Mother cheetah and cub, Kenya   Photograph by Anup & Manoj Shah/DRK Photo

May

6
monday

7
tuesday

8
wednesday

9
thursday

Sri Yukteswar's Birthday

10
friday

MAY

S	M	T	W	T	F	S
			1	2	3	4
5	6	7	8	9	10	11
12	13	14	15	16	17	18
19	20	21	22	23	24	25
26	27	28	29	30	31	

JUNE

S	M	T	W	T	F	S
						1
2	3	4	5	6	7	8
9	10	11	12	13	14	15
16	17	18	19	20	21	22
23/30	24	25	26	27	28	29

First Quarter ◐

11
saturday

Mother's Day (U.S., Canada, Australia, N.Z.)

12
sunday

May

13
monday

14
tuesday

15
wednesday

16
thursday

17
friday

18
saturday

Full Moon ○

19
sunday

May

S	M	T	W	T	F	S
			1	2	3	4
5	6	7	8	9	10	11
12	13	14	15	16	17	18
19	20	21	22	23	24	25
26	27	28	29	30	31	

June

S	M	T	W	T	F	S
						1
2	3	4	5	6	7	8
9	10	11	12	13	14	15
16	17	18	19	20	21	22
23/30	24	25	26	27	28	29

The valley of humbleness is filled with the joyous presence of God. When you enter the valley of meditation, you find it filled with the consciousness of God.

—Paramahansa Yogananda

Jungfrau Mountain with buttercups, Bernese Oberland, Switzerland Photograph by Patrick Frischknecht/AGE Fotostock

We can convert ourselves, our matter-of-fact workaday life, to vibrate with the song of the Infinite. Spiritualize yourself, so the divine melody will flow through your life no matter what your outer activities.

—Paramahansa Yogananda

Blue bunting on butterweed, Marion County, Illinois Photograph by Richard & Susan Day

May

Victoria Day (Canada)

20
monday

21
tuesday

22
wednesday

23
thursday

24
friday

MAY

S	M	T	W	T	F	S
			1	2	3	4
5	6	7	8	9	10	11
12	13	14	15	16	17	18
19	20	21	22	23	24	25
26	27	28	29	30	31	

JUNE

S	M	T	W	T	F	S
						1
2	3	4	5	6	7	8
9	10	11	12	13	14	15
16	17	18	19	20	21	22
23/30	24	25	26	27	28	29

25
saturday

Last Quarter ◑

26
sunday

May/June

27
monday
Memorial Day

28
tuesday

29
wednesday

30
thursday

31
friday

1
saturday

2
sunday

MAY

S	M	T	W	T	F	S
			1	2	3	4
5	6	7	8	9	10	11
12	13	14	15	16	17	18
19	20	21	22	23	24	25
26	27	28	29	30	31	

JUNE

S	M	T	W	T	F	S
						1
2	3	4	5	6	7	8
9	10	11	12	13	14	15
16	17	18	19	20	21	22
23/30	24	25	26	27	28	29

In the breeze I feel Thy touch;
In the sun, Thy warm love.
In the colorful scenery, I behold Thy beauty-face.

—Paramahansa Yogananda

Spring wildflowers, Carrizo Plain National Monument, California   Photograph by Dennis Frates

The invisible Mother is continuously expressing Herself in terms of visible forms — in flowers, mountains, seas, and stars.

—Paramahansa Yogananda

Mount Moran and lupines, Grand Teton National Park, Wyoming   Photograph by Fi Rust

June

New Moon ●

3 monday

4 tuesday

5 wednesday

6 thursday

7 friday

JUNE

S	M	T	W	T	F	S
						1
2	3	4	5	6	7	8
9	10	11	12	13	14	15
16	17	18	19	20	21	22
23/30	24	25	26	27	28	29

JULY

S	M	T	W	T	F	S
	1	2	3	4	5	6
7	8	9	10	11	12	13
14	15	16	17	18	19	20
21	22	23	24	25	26	27
28	29	30	31			

8 saturday

First Quarter ◐

9 sunday

June

10
monday

11
tuesday

12
wednesday

13
thursday

14
friday

15
saturday

16
sunday

Father's Day (U.S., Canada, U.K.)

June

S	M	T	W	T	F	S
						1
2	3	4	5	6	7	8
9	10	11	12	13	14	15
16	17	18	19	20	21	22
23/30	24	25	26	27	28	29

July

S	M	T	W	T	F	S
	1	2	3	4	5	6
7	8	9	10	11	12	13
14	15	16	17	18	19	20
21	22	23	24	25	26	27
28	29	30	31			

A body that is relaxed and calm invites mental peace.

—Paramahansa Yogananda

Napping koala bear, Victoria, Australia   Photograph by Gary Bell/Oceanwide Images

God says: "Follow the trail of beauty. I am hidden somewhere in its heart. I am Harmony, I am Love, I am Beauty, I am Fragrance, I am Joy."

—Paramahansa Yogananda

Phalaenopsis orchid   Photograph by Frans Lanting

June

17
monday

Full Moon ◯

18
tuesday

19
wednesday

20
thursday

21
friday

International Day of Yoga   Summer Solstice

22
saturday

23
sunday

June

S	M	T	W	T	F	S
						1
2	3	4	5	6	7	8
9	10	11	12	13	14	15
16	17	18	19	20	21	22
23/30	24	25	26	27	28	29

July

S	M	T	W	T	F	S
	1	2	3	4	5	6
7	8	9	10	11	12	13
14	15	16	17	18	19	20
21	22	23	24	25	26	27
28	29	30	31			

June

24
monday

25
tuesday
Last Quarter ◑

26
wednesday

27
thursday

28
friday

29
saturday

30
sunday

June

S	M	T	W	T	F	S
						1
2	3	4	5	6	7	8
9	10	11	12	13	14	15
16	17	18	19	20	21	22
23/30	24	25	26	27	28	29

July

S	M	T	W	T	F	S
	1	2	3	4	5	6
7	8	9	10	11	12	13
14	15	16	17	18	19	20
21	22	23	24	25	26	27
28	29	30	31			

Your real nature is calmness....It is time you remember who you are: the blessed soul, a reflection of Spirit.

—Paramahansa Yogananda

Lion pair, Okavango Delta, Botswana   Photograph by Wim van den Heever/Nature Picture Library

Though God is manifest everywhere, His essence is secreted behind the veil of Nature's phenomena.

—Paramahansa Yogananda

Tide pool, Yaquina Head, Oregon   Photograph by Dennis Frates

July

Canada Day (Canada)

1 monday

New Moon ●

2 tuesday

3 wednesday

Independence Day

4 thursday

5 friday

JULY

S	M	T	W	T	F	S
	1	2	3	4	5	6
7	8	9	10	11	12	13
14	15	16	17	18	19	20
21	22	23	24	25	26	27
28	29	30	31			

6 saturday

AUGUST

S	M	T	W	T	F	S
				1	2	3
4	5	6	7	8	9	10
11	12	13	14	15	16	17
18	19	20	21	22	23	24
25	26	27	28	29	30	31

7 sunday

July

8
monday

9
tuesday
First Quarter ◐

10
wednesday

11
thursday

12
friday

13
saturday

14
sunday

JULY

S	M	T	W	T	F	S
	1	2	3	4	5	6
7	8	9	10	11	12	13
14	15	16	17	18	19	20
21	22	23	24	25	26	27
28	29	30	31			

AUGUST

S	M	T	W	T	F	S
				1	2	3
4	5	6	7	8	9	10
11	12	13	14	15	16	17
18	19	20	21	22	23	24
25	26	27	28	29	30	31

If we are attuned to God, our perception is limitless,
pervading everywhere in the oceanic flow of the Divine Presence.

—Paramahansa Yogananda

Harris Beach State Park, Oregon   Photograph by Dennis Frates

When perfect friendship exists either between two hearts
or within a group of hearts in a spiritual relationship,
such friendship perfects each individual.

—Paramahansa Yogananda

California poppies   Photograph by Adam Gibbs

July

15
monday

16
tuesday

Full Moon ○

17
wednesday

18
thursday

19
friday

20
saturday

21
sunday

JULY

S	M	T	W	T	F	S
	1	2	3	4	5	6
7	8	9	10	11	12	13
14	15	16	17	18	19	20
21	22	23	24	25	26	27
28	29	30	31			

AUGUST

S	M	T	W	T	F	S
				1	2	3
4	5	6	7	8	9	10
11	12	13	14	15	16	17
18	19	20	21	22	23	24
25	26	27	28	29	30	31

July

22
monday

23
tuesday

24
wednesday

Last Quarter ◑

25
thursday

Mahavatar Babaji Commemoration Day

26
friday

27
saturday

28
sunday

July

S	M	T	W	T	F	S
	1	2	3	4	5	6
7	8	9	10	11	12	13
14	15	16	17	18	19	20
21	22	23	24	25	26	27
28	29	30	31			

August

S	M	T	W	T	F	S
				1	2	3
4	5	6	7	8	9	10
11	12	13	14	15	16	17
18	19	20	21	22	23	24
25	26	27	28	29	30	31

No power or miracles can compare with the joy that is God.
That perennial happiness is what everyone is seeking.

—Paramahansa Yogananda

Victoria Falls, Zimbabwe Photograph by Andrew Woodley/AGE Fotostock

If you need respite from inharmonies...
go to some peaceful place and stay alone for a while,
listening to the soft sounds of nature and of God within.

—Paramahansa Yogananda

Australian king parrot, Victoria, Australia   Photograph by Greg Oakley/Minden Pictures

July/August

29
monday

30
tuesday

31
wednesday

New Moon ●

1
thursday

2
friday

3
saturday

4
sunday

July

S	M	T	W	T	F	S
	1	2	3	4	5	6
7	8	9	10	11	12	13
14	15	16	17	18	19	20
21	22	23	24	25	26	27
28	29	30	31			

August

S	M	T	W	T	F	S
				1	2	3
4	5	6	7	8	9	10
11	12	13	14	15	16	17
18	19	20	21	22	23	24
25	26	27	28	29	30	31

August

5
monday

6
tuesday

7
wednesday

First Quarter ◐

8
thursday

9
friday

10
saturday

11
sunday

AUGUST

S	M	T	W	T	F	S
				1	2	3
4	5	6	7	8	9	10
11	12	13	14	15	16	17
18	19	20	21	22	23	24
25	26	27	28	29	30	31

SEPTEMBER

S	M	T	W	T	F	S
1	2	3	4	5	6	7
8	9	10	11	12	13	14
15	16	17	18	19	20	21
22	23	24	25	26	27	28
29	30					

All life is a school of experience that points in one direction: Godward.

—Paramahansa Yogananda

Castle Rock, Echo Creek, Utah Photograph by Londie G. Padelsky

We must learn to live more consciously, more understandingly,
if we are to get along in a better way in this world.

—Paramahansa Yogananda

Pelicans and seagulls share a dinghy, New South Wales, Australia Photograph by Gary Bell/Oceanwide Images

August

12
monday

13
tuesday

14
wednesday

Full Moon ○

15
thursday

16
friday

August

S	M	T	W	T	F	S
				1	2	3
4	5	6	7	8	9	10
11	12	13	14	15	16	17
18	19	20	21	22	23	24
25	26	27	28	29	30	31

September

S	M	T	W	T	F	S
1	2	3	4	5	6	7
8	9	10	11	12	13	14
15	16	17	18	19	20	21
22	23	24	25	26	27	28
29	30					

17
saturday

18
sunday

August

19
monday

20
tuesday

21
wednesday

22
thursday

23
friday

Last Quarter ◑

24
saturday

Janmashtami

25
sunday

August

S	M	T	W	T	F	S
				1	2	3
4	5	6	7	8	9	10
11	12	13	14	15	16	17
18	19	20	21	22	23	24
25	26	27	28	29	30	31

September

S	M	T	W	T	F	S
1	2	3	4	5	6	7
8	9	10	11	12	13	14
15	16	17	18	19	20	21
22	23	24	25	26	27	28
29	30					

*I*n the stillness of my soul I humbly bow before Thine omnipresence, knowing that Thou art ever leading me onward and upward on the path of Self-realization.

—Paramahansa Yogananda

Grand Teton National Park, Wyoming   Photograph by Steve Guadarrama

My dreams of perfection are bridges that carry me into the realm of pure ideas.

—Paramahansa Yogananda

Turret Arch, Arches National Park, Utah   Photograph by Dave Welling

August/September

26
monday

27
tuesday

28
wednesday

29
thursday

30
friday

New Moon ●

31
saturday

1
sunday

AUGUST

S	M	T	W	T	F	S
				1	2	3
4	5	6	7	8	9	10
11	12	13	14	15	16	17
18	19	20	21	22	23	24
25	26	27	28	29	30	31

SEPTEMBER

S	M	T	W	T	F	S
1	2	3	4	5	6	7
8	9	10	11	12	13	14
15	16	17	18	19	20	21
22	23	24	25	26	27	28
29	30					

September

2
monday

Labor Day (U.S. and Canada)

3
tuesday

4
wednesday

5
thursday

First Quarter ◐

6
friday

7
saturday

8
sunday

SEPTEMBER

S	M	T	W	T	F	S
1	2	3	4	5	6	7
8	9	10	11	12	13	14
15	16	17	18	19	20	21
22	23	24	25	26	27	28
29	30					

OCTOBER

S	M	T	W	T	F	S
		1	2	3	4	5
6	7	8	9	10	11	12
13	14	15	16	17	18	19
20	21	22	23	24	25	26
27	28	29	30	31		

The soul has no particular apparel; it can don any style it wants to.
The body is limited, but the soul can put on any kind of mental dress,
any kind of personality.

—Paramahansa Yogananda

Malachite butterfly, Florida   Photograph by Darrell Gulin/DRK Photo

Those who on earth attain valiant victory over darkness will bask in the light and glory of a tangible peace and inner happiness.

—Paramahansa Yogananda

Gemsbok, Namib Desert, Namibia Photograph by Martin Harvey/DRK Photo

September

9
monday

10
tuesday

11
wednesday

12
thursday

13
friday

Full Moon ○

September

S	M	T	W	T	F	S
1	2	3	4	5	6	7
8	9	10	11	12	13	14
15	16	17	18	19	20	21
22	23	24	25	26	27	28
29	30					

October

S	M	T	W	T	F	S
		1	2	3	4	5
6	7	8	9	10	11	12
13	14	15	16	17	18	19
20	21	22	23	24	25	26
27	28	29	30	31		

14
saturday

15
sunday

September

16
monday

17
tuesday

18
wednesday

19
thursday

20
friday

21
saturday

U.N. International Day of Peace   Last Quarter ◑

22
sunday

September

S	M	T	W	T	F	S
1	2	3	4	5	6	7
8	9	10	11	12	13	14
15	16	17	18	19	20	21
22	23	24	25	26	27	28
29	30					

October

S	M	T	W	T	F	S
		1	2	3	4	5
6	7	8	9	10	11	12
13	14	15	16	17	18	19
20	21	22	23	24	25	26
27	28	29	30	31		

The breeze of Thy love wafts through me, O Father,
and the leaves of the tree of my life gently tremble
in response to Thy coming.

—Paramahansa Yogananda

Japanese red maple leaves, Seabeck, Washington Photograph by Don Paulson

The countless forms in Nature are expressions of Thy versatile genius — originals from Thy ceaselessly vibrating fingers.
May we see in all creation Thine inimitable handiwork.

—Paramahansa Yogananda

Weathered sandstone, Upper Antelope Canyon, Arizona   Photograph by Juan Carlos Muñoz/AGE Fotostock

September

23
monday
Autumnal Equinox

24
tuesday

25
wednesday

26
thursday
Lahiri Mahasaya's Mahasamadhi

27
friday

28
saturday
New Moon ●

29
sunday
Rosh Hashanah

September

S	M	T	W	T	F	S
1	2	3	4	5	6	7
8	9	10	11	12	13	14
15	16	17	18	19	20	21
22	23	24	25	26	27	28
29	30					

October

S	M	T	W	T	F	S
		1	2	3	4	5
6	7	8	9	10	11	12
13	14	15	16	17	18	19
20	21	22	23	24	25	26
27	28	29	30	31		

September/October

30
monday

Lahiri Mahasaya's Birthday

1
tuesday

2
wednesday

3
thursday

4
friday

5
saturday

First Quarter ◐

6
sunday

September

S	M	T	W	T	F	S
1	2	3	4	5	6	7
8	9	10	11	12	13	14
15	16	17	18	19	20	21
22	23	24	25	26	27	28
29	30					

October

S	M	T	W	T	F	S
		1	2	3	4	5
6	7	8	9	10	11	12
13	14	15	16	17	18	19
20	21	22	23	24	25	26
27	28	29	30	31		

Life is entertaining when we do not take it too seriously.

—Paramahansa Yogananda

Red panda, Zurich Zoo, Switzerland   Photograph by Emmanuel Keller/AKM Images

No matter where you go, your wandering footsteps will lead you back to God.
There is no other way to go.

—Paramahansa Yogananda

Algonquin Provincial Park, Ontario, Canada   Photograph by Kevin McNeal

October

7
monday

8
tuesday
Yom Kippur

9
wednesday

10
thursday

11
friday

12
saturday

13
sunday
Full Moon ○

OCTOBER

S	M	T	W	T	F	S
		1	2	3	4	5
6	7	8	9	10	11	12
13	14	15	16	17	18	19
20	21	22	23	24	25	26
27	28	29	30	31		

NOVEMBER

S	M	T	W	T	F	S
					1	2
3	4	5	6	7	8	9
10	11	12	13	14	15	16
17	18	19	20	21	22	23
24	25	26	27	28	29	30

October

14
monday

Columbus Day Thanksgiving Day (Canada)

15
tuesday

16
wednesday

17
thursday

18
friday

19
saturday

20
sunday

October

S	M	T	W	T	F	S
		1	2	3	4	5
6	7	8	9	10	11	12
13	14	15	16	17	18	19
20	21	22	23	24	25	26
27	28	29	30	31		

November

S	M	T	W	T	F	S
					1	2
3	4	5	6	7	8	9
10	11	12	13	14	15	16
17	18	19	20	21	22	23
24	25	26	27	28	29	30

Your

2020 Inner Reflections Engagement Calendar

is now available online and in select bookstores.

You may also place your order directly from Self-Realization Fellowship
by calling 818-549-5151 Monday – Friday from 9:00 a.m. to 5:00 p.m. Pacific time
or order online at:
www.srfbooks.org

If you would like a free copy of Self-Realization Fellowship's complete
catalog of books and recordings, please request it by phone or
fill out the form below and fax or mail it to:

Self-Realization Fellowship
3880 San Rafael Ave.
Los Angeles, CA 90065-3219 U.S.A.
Fax: 800-801-1952

Name: ____

Address: ____

City: ______________________ State: _____ Zip code: __________

Daytime phone: ___________________ Date: __________________

In the limpid waters of my soul let me behold the unruffled reflections of Thy face of stillness.

—Paramahansa Yogananda

Ellis Pond, Maine   Photograph by Paul Rezendes

Meditate, and you will realize the omnipresent Absolute Truth
and see Its mysterious workings in your life
and in all the glories of creation.

—Paramahansa Yogananda

Aurora borealis over Lofoten Islands, Norway Photograph by Tom Mackie

October

21
monday

Last Quarter ◑

22
tuesday

23
wednesday

24
thursday

25
friday

OCTOBER

S	M	T	W	T	F	S
		1	2	3	4	5
6	7	8	9	10	11	12
13	14	15	16	17	18	19
20	21	22	23	24	25	26
27	28	29	30	31		

NOVEMBER

S	M	T	W	T	F	S
					1	2
3	4	5	6	7	8	9
10	11	12	13	14	15	16
17	18	19	20	21	22	23
24	25	26	27	28	29	30

26
saturday

27
sunday

Daylight Saving Time ends (European Union) New Moon ●

October/November

28
monday

29
tuesday

30
wednesday

31
thursday

Halloween (U.S., Canada, U.K.)

1
friday

2
saturday

3
sunday

Daylight Saving Time ends (U.S. and Canada)

October

S	M	T	W	T	F	S
		1	2	3	4	5
6	7	8	9	10	11	12
13	14	15	16	17	18	19
20	21	22	23	24	25	26
27	28	29	30	31		

November

S	M	T	W	T	F	S
					1	2
3	4	5	6	7	8	9
10	11	12	13	14	15	16
17	18	19	20	21	22	23
24	25	26	27	28	29	30

The eyes clearly reflect what you are within.
So there is but one method that can beautify the life and expression in the eyes:
the inner cultivation of beautiful thoughts and feelings.

—Paramahansa Yogananda

Northern saw-whet owl, Colorado   Photograph by Dave Welling

As you look upon creation, which appears so solid and real,
remember always to think of it as the thought of God,
frozen into physical forms.

—Paramahansa Yogananda

Chinstrap penguins and icebergs, Antarctica   Photograph by Frans Lanting

November

4
monday

First Quarter ◐

5
tuesday

General Election Day

6
wednesday

7
thursday

8
friday

NOVEMBER

S	M	T	W	T	F	S
					1	2
3	4	5	6	7	8	9
10	11	12	13	14	15	16
17	18	19	20	21	22	23
24	25	26	27	28	29	30

DECEMBER

S	M	T	W	T	F	S
1	2	3	4	5	6	7
8	9	10	11	12	13	14
15	16	17	18	19	20	21
22	23	24	25	26	27	28
29	30	31				

9
saturday

10
sunday

Remembrance Day (U.K.)

November

11
monday

Veterans Day   Remembrance Day (Canada)

12
tuesday

Full Moon ○

13
wednesday

14
thursday

15
friday

16
saturday

17
sunday

November

S	M	T	W	T	F	S
					1	2
3	4	5	6	7	8	9
10	11	12	13	14	15	16
17	18	19	20	21	22	23
24	25	26	27	28	29	30

December

S	M	T	W	T	F	S
1	2	3	4	5	6	7
8	9	10	11	12	13	14
15	16	17	18	19	20	21
22	23	24	25	26	27	28
29	30	31				

God is the joy of meditation, He is the love flowing through all hearts,
He is the life throbbing in every living thing.

—Paramahansa Yogananda

Junction Creek, Ontario, Canada   Photograph by Don Johnston/AGE Fotostock

Environment is of supreme importance to spiritual progress.
It is greater than will power....Surround yourself with a good environment.

—Paramahansa Yogananda

Windsor County, Vermont   Photograph by Kevin McNeal

November

18
monday

19
tuesday

Last Quarter ◑

20
wednesday

21
thursday

22
friday

NOVEMBER

S	M	T	W	T	F	S
					1	2
3	4	5	6	7	8	9
10	11	12	13	14	15	16
17	18	19	20	21	22	23
24	25	26	27	28	29	30

DECEMBER

S	M	T	W	T	F	S
1	2	3	4	5	6	7
8	9	10	11	12	13	14
15	16	17	18	19	20	21
22	23	24	25	26	27	28
29	30	31				

23
saturday

24
sunday

November/December

25
monday

26
tuesday

New Moon ●

27
wednesday

28
thursday

Thanksgiving Day

29
friday

30
saturday

1
sunday

November

S	M	T	W	T	F	S
					1	2
3	4	5	6	7	8	9
10	11	12	13	14	15	16
17	18	19	20	21	22	23
24	25	26	27	28	29	30

December

S	M	T	W	T	F	S
1	2	3	4	5	6	7
8	9	10	11	12	13	14
15	16	17	18	19	20	21
22	23	24	25	26	27	28
29	30	31				

Always in the background of your mind
hum a silent devotional song of love to your beloved Heavenly Father,
remembering that all your abilities are gifts from Him.

—Paramahansa Yogananda

Canadian geese at sunrise Photograph by William Houghton/AKM Images

Beginning with the early dawn each day,
I will radiate my cheer to everyone I meet today.
I will be the mental sunshine for all who cross my path.

—Paramahansa Yogananda

Yoho National Park, British Columbia, Canada   Photograph by Tom Mackie

December

2
monday

3
tuesday

First Quarter ◐

4
wednesday

5
thursday

6
friday

7
saturday

8
sunday

DECEMBER

S	M	T	W	T	F	S
1	2	3	4	5	6	7
8	9	10	11	12	13	14
15	16	17	18	19	20	21
22	23	24	25	26	27	28
29	30	31				

JANUARY 2020

S	M	T	W	T	F	S
			1	2	3	4
5	6	7	8	9	10	11
12	13	14	15	16	17	18
19	20	21	22	23	24	25
26	27	28	29	30	31	

December

9
monday

10
tuesday

11
wednesday

Full Moon ○

12
thursday

13
friday

14
saturday

15
sunday

DECEMBER

S	M	T	W	T	F	S
1	2	3	4	5	6	7
8	9	10	11	12	13	14
15	16	17	18	19	20	21
22	23	24	25	26	27	28
29	30	31				

JANUARY 2020

S	M	T	W	T	F	S
			1	2	3	4
5	6	7	8	9	10	11
12	13	14	15	16	17	18
19	20	21	22	23	24	25
26	27	28	29	30	31	

God is the mirror of silence in which all creation is reflected.

—Paramahansa Yogananda

Banff National Park, Alberta, Canada   Photograph by Mike Grandmaison

Every morning when you awaken, you should resolve:
"Today I am going to be cheerful. No matter what happens, I will be cheerful."

—Paramahansa Yogananda

Northern male cardinal, Freeville, New York   Photograph by Marie Read/AnimalsAnimals

December

16
monday

17
tuesday

Last Quarter ◑

18
wednesday

19
thursday

20
friday

DECEMBER

S	M	T	W	T	F	S
1	2	3	4	5	6	7
8	9	10	11	12	13	14
15	16	17	18	19	20	21
22	23	24	25	26	27	28
29	30	31				

JANUARY 2020

S	M	T	W	T	F	S
			1	2	3	4
5	6	7	8	9	10	11
12	13	14	15	16	17	18
19	20	21	22	23	24	25
26	27	28	29	30	31	

Winter Solstice

21
saturday

Hanukkah

22
sunday

December

23
monday

24
tuesday

25
wednesday

Christmas New Moon ●

26
thursday

Boxing Day (Canada, U.K., Australia, N.Z.)

27
friday

28
saturday

29
sunday

DECEMBER

S	M	T	W	T	F	S
1	2	3	4	5	6	7
8	9	10	11	12	13	14
15	16	17	18	19	20	21
22	23	24	25	26	27	28
29	30	31				

JANUARY 2020

S	M	T	W	T	F	S
			1	2	3	4
5	6	7	8	9	10	11
12	13	14	15	16	17	18
19	20	21	22	23	24	25
26	27	28	29	30	31	

Start the Christmas season and New Year with a new light of understanding. Meditate daily, and one day a week dedicate several hours to deep communion and talking with God; and you will have a life that you never before thought could be yours.

—Paramahansa Yogananda

Banff National Park, Alberta, Canada   Photograph by Tom Mackie

Heavenly Father, I will develop Thy gift of good memory by recalling all the beautiful things that have happened in my life.

—Paramahansa Yogananda

King penguins, St. Andrews Bay, South Georgia   Photograph by Daisy Gilardini

December/January

30
monday

31
tuesday

New Year's Day
1
wednesday

First Quarter ◐
2
thursday

3
friday

DECEMBER

S	M	T	W	T	F	S
1	2	3	4	5	6	7
8	9	10	11	12	13	14
15	16	17	18	19	20	21
22	23	24	25	26	27	28
29	30	31				

4
saturday

JANUARY 2020

S	M	T	W	T	F	S
			1	2	3	4
5	6	7	8	9	10	11
12	13	14	15	16	17	18
19	20	21	22	23	24	25
26	27	28	29	30	31	

Paramahansa Yogananda's Birthday
5
sunday

NOTES

ACKNOWLEDGMENTS

We wish to express our sincere appreciation to the following photographers and agencies who contributed to this year's *Inner Reflections* engagement calendar. Following a contributor's name, in parentheses, is the month and a day of the week, or other description, where each photo appears.

AGE Fotostock (1/7, 4/8, 5/13, 7/22, 9/23, 11/11)

AKM Images (2/11, 9/30, 11/25)

Animals Animals (1/21, 12/16)

Mary Liz Austin (4/22)

Robert Barber/AKM Images (2/11)

Gary Bell/Oceanwide Images (6/10, 8/12)

Thomas Cooper (3/11)

Richard & Susan Day (3/25, 5/20)

DRK Photo (5/6, 9/2, 9/9)

Guy Edwardes (4/29)

Tim Fitzharris/Minden Pictures (1/28)

Dennis Frates (5/27, 7/1, 7/8)

Patrick Frischknecht/AGE Fotostock (5/13)

Howie Garber/AnimalsAnimals (1/21)

Adam Gibbs (7/15)

Daisy Gilardini (12/30)

Mike Grandmaison (12/9)

Steve Guadarrama (8/19)

Darrell Gulin/DRK Photo (9/2)

Martin Harvey/DRK Photo (9/9)

Wim van den Heever/Nature Picture Library (6/24)

John Hendrickson (2/25)

William Houghton/AKM Images (11/25)

Don Johnston/AGE Fotostock (11/11)

Emmanuel Keller/AKM Images (9/30)

Frans Lanting (12/31/2018, 6/17, 11/4)

Tom Mackie (Cover, 3/18, 10/21, 12/2, 12/23)

Kevin McNeal (10/7, 11/18)

Minden Pictures (1/28, 7/29)

Juan Carlos Muñoz/AGE Fotostock (9/23)

Nature Picture Library (6/24)

Greg Oakley/Minden Pictures (7/29)

Oceanwide Images (6/10, 8/12)

Londie G. Padelsky (1/14, 3/4, 4/15, 8/5)

Don Paulson (9/16)

Marie Read/Animals Animals (12/16)

Paul Rezendes (4/1, 10/14)

Fi Rust (6/3)

Anup & Manoj Shah/DRK Photo (5/6)

N. Sorokin/AGE Fotostock (1/7)

Tom Till (2/4)

Dave Welling (8/26, 10/28)

Michael Wheatley (2/18)

Michael Wheatley/AGE Fotostock (4/8)

Andrew Woodley/AGE Fotostock (7/22)

About Paramahansa Yogananda

Paramahansa Yogananda
1893-1952

All the quotes featured in *Inner Reflections* have been selected from the writings of Paramahansa Yogananda, one of the preeminent spiritual teachers of the 20th century. Yogananda came to the United States in 1920 as India's delegate to an international congress of religious leaders convening in Boston. He remained in the West for the better part of the next thirty-two years, conducting classes in cities across America, counseling, and creating a monumental body of written work.

Paramahansa Yogananda's life story, *Autobiography of a Yogi*, is considered a modern spiritual classic. It was selected one of "The Top 100 Spiritual Books of the Twentieth Century" in a survey conducted by HarperCollins. A perennial best seller since it was first published in 1946, *Autobiography of a Yogi* has been translated into more than forty languages and is widely used in college and university courses.

An award-winning documentary film about Paramahansa Yogananda's life and work, *Awake: The Life of Yogananda*, was released in October 2014.

For more information about SRF publications and the teachings of Paramahansa Yogananda, please visit our website:

www.yogananda-srf.org

Self-Realization Fellowship
FOUNDED 1920 BY PARAMAHANSA YOGANANDA

SELF-REALIZATION FELLOWSHIP, the international nonprofit society founded by Paramahansa Yogananda, is dedicated to carrying on his spiritual and humanitarian work — fostering a spirit of greater harmony and understanding among those of all nations and faiths, and introducing truth-seekers around the world to his universal teachings on the ancient science of Yoga.

A SELECTION OF BOOKS BY PARAMAHANSA YOGANANDA

Available at bookstores or from our website:
www.srfbooks.org

Autobiography of a Yogi

Autobiography of a Yogi *(Audiobook, read by Sir Ben Kingsley)*

The Science of Religion

The Law of Success

How You Can Talk With God

Metaphysical Meditations

Where There Is Light: *Insight and Inspiration for Meeting Life's Challenges*

The Yoga of Jesus: *Understanding the Hidden Teachings of the Gospels*

The Yoga of the Bhagavad Gita: *An Introduction to India's Universal Science of God-Realization*

The Collected Talks and Essays
Volume I: Man's Eternal Quest
Volume II: The Divine Romance
Volume III: Journey to Self-realization

DVD VIDEO

Awake: The Life of Yogananda
A film by CounterPoint Films

SELF-REALIZATION FELLOWSHIP LESSONS

The scientific techniques of meditation taught by Paramahansa Yogananda, including *Kriya Yoga* — as well as his guidance on all aspects of balanced spiritual living — are taught in the *Self-Realization Fellowship Lessons.* A free introductory booklet, *Undreamed-of Possibilities,* is available on our website www.yogananda-srf.org.

SELF-REALIZATION FELLOWSHIP

3880 San Rafael Avenue • Los Angeles, CA 90065-3219

TEL (323) 225-2471 • FAX (323) 225-5088

www.yogananda-srf.org

2018

January

s	m	t	w	t	f	s
	1	2	3	4	5	6
7	8	9	10	11	12	13
14	15	16	17	18	19	20
21	22	23	24	25	26	27
28	29	30	31			

February

s	m	t	w	t	f	s
				1	2	3
4	5	6	7	8	9	10
11	12	13	14	15	16	17
18	19	20	21	22	23	24
25	26	27	28			

March

s	m	t	w	t	f	s
				1	2	3
4	5	6	7	8	9	10
11	12	13	14	15	16	17
18	19	20	21	22	23	24
25	26	27	28	29	30	31

April

s	m	t	w	t	f	s
1	2	3	4	5	6	7
8	9	10	11	12	13	14
15	16	17	18	19	20	21
22	23	24	25	26	27	28
29	30					

May

s	m	t	w	t	f	s
		1	2	3	4	5
6	7	8	9	10	11	12
13	14	15	16	17	18	19
20	21	22	23	24	25	26
27	28	29	30	31		

June

s	m	t	w	t	f	s
					1	2
3	4	5	6	7	8	9
10	11	12	13	14	15	16
17	18	19	20	21	22	23
24	25	26	27	28	29	30

July

s	m	t	w	t	f	s
1	2	3	4	5	6	7
8	9	10	11	12	13	14
15	16	17	18	19	20	21
22	23	24	25	26	27	28
29	30	31				

August

s	m	t	w	t	f	s
			1	2	3	4
5	6	7	8	9	10	11
12	13	14	15	16	17	18
19	20	21	22	23	24	25
26	27	28	29	30	31	

September

s	m	t	w	t	f	s
						1
2	3	4	5	6	7	8
9	10	11	12	13	14	15
16	17	18	19	20	21	22
23/30	24	25	26	27	28	29

October

s	m	t	w	t	f	s
	1	2	3	4	5	6
7	8	9	10	11	12	13
14	15	16	17	18	19	20
21	22	23	24	25	26	27
28	29	30	31			

November

s	m	t	w	t	f	s
				1	2	3
4	5	6	7	8	9	10
11	12	13	14	15	16	17
18	19	20	21	22	23	24
25	26	27	28	29	30	

December

s	m	t	w	t	f	s
						1
2	3	4	5	6	7	8
9	10	11	12	13	14	15
16	17	18	19	20	21	22
23/30	24/31	25	26	27	28	29

2020

January

s	m	t	w	t	f	s
			1	2	3	4
5	6	7	8	9	10	11
12	13	14	15	16	17	18
19	20	21	22	23	24	25
26	27	28	29	30	31	

February

s	m	t	w	t	f	s
						1
2	3	4	5	6	7	8
9	10	11	12	13	14	15
16	17	18	19	20	21	22
23	24	25	26	27	28	29

March

s	m	t	w	t	f	s
1	2	3	4	5	6	7
8	9	10	11	12	13	14
15	16	17	18	19	20	21
22	23	24	25	26	27	28
29	30	31				

April

s	m	t	w	t	f	s
			1	2	3	4
5	6	7	8	9	10	11
12	13	14	15	16	17	18
19	20	21	22	23	24	25
26	27	28	29	30		

May

s	m	t	w	t	f	s
					1	2
3	4	5	6	7	8	9
10	11	12	13	14	15	16
17	18	19	20	21	22	23
24/31	25	26	27	28	29	30

June

s	m	t	w	t	f	s
	1	2	3	4	5	6
7	8	9	10	11	12	13
14	15	16	17	18	19	20
21	22	23	24	25	26	27
28	29	30				

July

s	m	t	w	t	f	s
			1	2	3	4
5	6	7	8	9	10	11
12	13	14	15	16	17	18
19	20	21	22	23	24	25
26	27	28	29	30	31	

August

s	m	t	w	t	f	s
						1
2	3	4	5	6	7	8
9	10	11	12	13	14	15
16	17	18	19	20	21	22
23/30	24/31	25	26	27	28	29

September

s	m	t	w	t	f	s
		1	2	3	4	5
6	7	8	9	10	11	12
13	14	15	16	17	18	19
20	21	22	23	24	25	26
27	28	29	30			

October

s	m	t	w	t	f	s
				1	2	3
4	5	6	7	8	9	10
11	12	13	14	15	16	17
18	19	20	21	22	23	24
25	26	27	28	29	30	31

November

s	m	t	w	t	f	s
1	2	3	4	5	6	7
8	9	10	11	12	13	14
15	16	17	18	19	20	21
22	23	24	25	26	27	28
29	30					

December

s	m	t	w	t	f	s
		1	2	3	4	5
6	7	8	9	10	11	12
13	14	15	16	17	18	19
20	21	22	23	24	25	26
27	28	29	30	31		

2019

January

s	m	t	w	t	f	s
		1	2	3	4	5
6	7	8	9	10	11	12
13	14	15	16	17	18	19
20	21	22	23	24	25	26
27	28	29	30	31		

February

s	m	t	w	t	f	s
					1	2
3	4	5	6	7	8	9
10	11	12	13	14	15	16
17	18	19	20	21	22	23
24	25	26	27	28		

March

s	m	t	w	t	f	s
					1	2
3	4	5	6	7	8	9
10	11	12	13	14	15	16
17	18	19	20	21	22	23
24/31	25	26	27	28	29	30

April

s	m	t	w	t	f	s
	1	2	3	4	5	6
7	8	9	10	11	12	13
14	15	16	17	18	19	20
21	22	23	24	25	26	27
28	29	30				

May

s	m	t	w	t	f	s
			1	2	3	4
5	6	7	8	9	10	11
12	13	14	15	16	17	18
19	20	21	22	23	24	25
26	27	28	29	30	31	

June

s	m	t	w	t	f	s
						1
2	3	4	5	6	7	8
9	10	11	12	13	14	15
16	17	18	19	20	21	22
23/30	24	25	26	27	28	29

July

s	m	t	w	t	f	s
	1	2	3	4	5	6
7	8	9	10	11	12	13
14	15	16	17	18	19	20
21	22	23	24	25	26	27
28	29	30	31			

August

s	m	t	w	t	f	s
				1	2	3
4	5	6	7	8	9	10
11	12	13	14	15	16	17
18	19	20	21	22	23	24
25	26	27	28	29	30	31

September

s	m	t	w	t	f	s
1	2	3	4	5	6	7
8	9	10	11	12	13	14
15	16	17	18	19	20	21
22	23	24	25	26	27	28
29	30					

October

s	m	t	w	t	f	s
		1	2	3	4	5
6	7	8	9	10	11	12
13	14	15	16	17	18	19
20	21	22	23	24	25	26
27	28	29	30	31		

November

s	m	t	w	t	f	s
					1	2
3	4	5	6	7	8	9
10	11	12	13	14	15	16
17	18	19	20	21	22	23
24	25	26	27	28	29	30

December

s	m	t	w	t	f	s
1	2	3	4	5	6	7
8	9	10	11	12	13	14
15	16	17	18	19	20	21
22	23	24	25	26	27	28
29	30	31				

January

Sunday	Monday	Tuesday	Wednesday	Thursday	Friday	Saturday
		1	2	3	4	5
6	7	8	9	10	11	12
13	14	15	16	17	18	19
20	21	22	23	24	25	26
27	28	29	30	31		

Jan. 1 New Year's Day
Jan. 5 Paramahansa Yogananda's Birthday
Jan. 21 Martin Luther King, Jr.'s Birthday (Observed)
Jan. 26 Australia Day (Australia)

February

Sunday	Monday	Tuesday	Wednesday	Thursday	Friday	Saturday
					1	2
3	4	5	6	7	8	9
10	11	12	13	14	15	16
17	18	19	20	21	22	23
24	25	26	27	28		

Feb. 14 St. Valentine's Day
Feb. 18 Presidents' Day

March

Sunday	Monday	Tuesday	Wednesday	Thursday	Friday	Saturday
					1	2
3	4	5	6	7	8	9
10	11	12	13	14	15	16
17	18	19	20	21	22	23
24	25	26	27	28	29	30
31						

March 7 Paramahansa Yogananda's Mahasamadhi
March 9 Sri Yukteswar's Mahasamadhi
March 10 Daylight Saving Time begins (U.S. and Canada)
March 17 St. Patrick's Day
March 20 Vernal Equinox
March 31 Daylight Savings Time begins (European Union)

April

Sunday	Monday	Tuesday	Wednesday	Thursday	Friday	Saturday
	1	2	3	4	5	6
7	8	9	10	11	12	13
14	15	16	17	18	19	20
21	22	23	24	25	26	27
28	29	30				

April 19 Good Friday
Passover begins

April 21 Easter Sunday

April 22 Easter Monday (All except U.S. and Scotland)
Earth Day

May

Sunday	Monday	Tuesday	Wednesday	Thursday	Friday	Saturday
			1	2	3	4
5	6	7	8	9	10	11
12	13	14	15	16	17	18
19	20	21	22	23	24	25
26	27	28	29	30	31	

May 2 National Day of Prayer
May 10 Sri Yukteswar's Birthday
May 12 Mother's Day (U.S., Canada, Australia, N.Z.)
May 20 Victoria Day (Canada)
May 27 Memorial Day

JUNE

Sunday	Monday	Tuesday	Wednesday	Thursday	Friday	Saturday
						1
2	3	4	5	6	7	8
9	10	11	12	13	14	15
16	17	18	19	20	21	22
23	24	25	26	27	28	29
30						

June 16 Father's Day (U.S., Canada, U.K.)

June 21 Summer Solstice
International Day of Yoga

July

Sunday	Monday	Tuesday	Wednesday	Thursday	Friday	Saturday
	1	2	3	4	5	6
7	8	9	10	11	12	13
14	15	16	17	18	19	20
21	22	23	24	25	26	27
28	29	30	31			

July 1 Canada Day (Canada)
July 4 Independence Day
July 25 Mahavatar Babaji Commemoration Day

AUGUST

Sunday	Monday	Tuesday	Wednesday	Thursday	Friday	Saturday
				1	2	3
4	5	6	7	8	9	10
11	12	13	14	15	16	17
18	19	20	21	22	23	24
25	26	27	28	29	30	31

Aug. 24 Janmashtami

September

Sunday	Monday	Tuesday	Wednesday	Thursday	Friday	Saturday
1	2	3	4	5	6	7
8	9	10	11	12	13	14
15	16	17	18	19	20	21
22	23	24	25	26	27	28
29	30					

Sept. 2 Labor Day (U.S. and Canada)
Sept. 21 U.N. International Day of Peace
Sept. 23 Autumnal Equinox
Sept. 26 Lahiri Mahasaya's Mahasamadhi
Sept. 29 Rosh Hashanah
Sept. 30 Lahiri Mahasaya's Birthday

OCTOBER

Sunday	Monday	Tuesday	Wednesday	Thursday	Friday	Saturday
		1	2	3	4	5
6	7	8	9	10	11	12
13	14	15	16	17	18	19
20	21	22	23	24	25	26
27	28	29	30	31		

Oct. 8 Yom Kippur

Oct. 14 Columbus Day
Thanksgiving Day (Canada)

Oct. 27 Daylight Saving Time ends (European Union)

Oct. 31 Halloween (U.S., Canada, U.K.)

November

Sunday	Monday	Tuesday	Wednesday	Thursday	Friday	Saturday
					1	2
3	4	5	6	7	8	9
10	11	12	13	14	15	16
17	18	19	20	21	22	23
24	25	26	27	28	29	30

Nov. 3 Daylight Saving Time ends (U.S. and Canada)
Nov. 5 General Election Day
Nov. 10 Remembrance Day (U.K.)
Nov. 11 Veterans Day
Remembrance Day (Canada)
Nov. 28 Thanksgiving Day

December

Sunday	Monday	Tuesday	Wednesday	Thursday	Friday	Saturday
1	2	3	4	5	6	7
8	9	10	11	12	13	14
15	16	17	18	19	20	21
22	23	24	25	26	27	28
29	30	31				

Dec. 21 Winter Solstice
Dec. 22 Hanukkah
Dec. 25 Christmas
Dec. 26 Boxing Day (Canada, U.K., Australia, N.Z.)

NOTES